Calming
Nature

igloobooks

Published in 2020
by Igloo Books Ltd
Cottage Farm
Sywell
NN6 0BJ
www.igloobooks.com

0720 003
8 10 11 9 7
ISBN: 978-1-78557-745-1

Designed by Charles Wood-Penn
Edited by Vicky Taylor

Interiors illustrated by Ashish Dhir
All other images: © iStock / Getty

Printed and manufactured in China

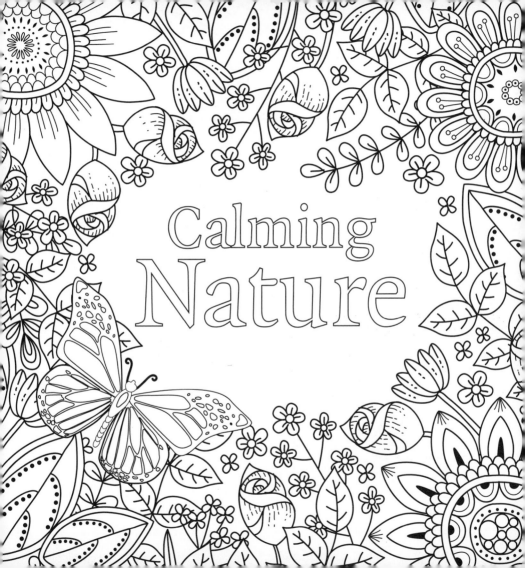

Calming Nature

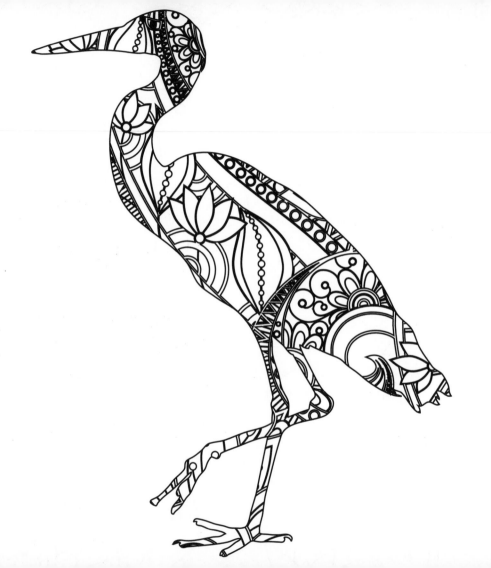

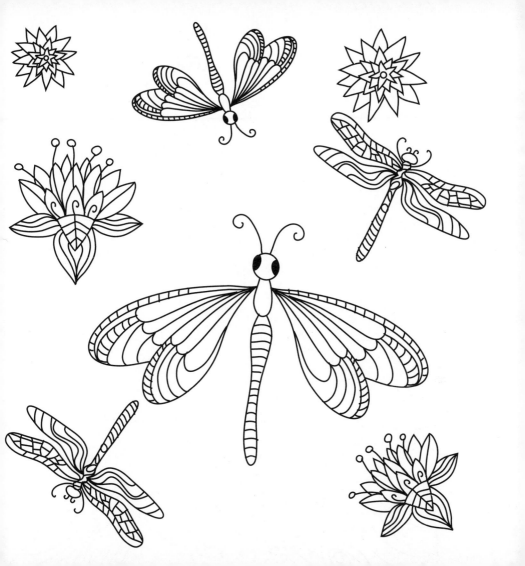

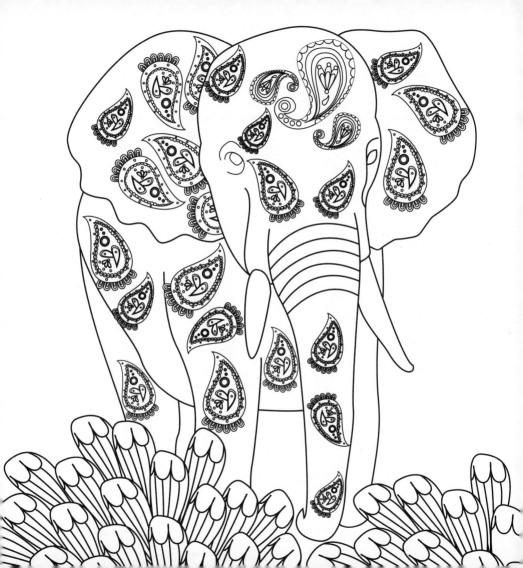

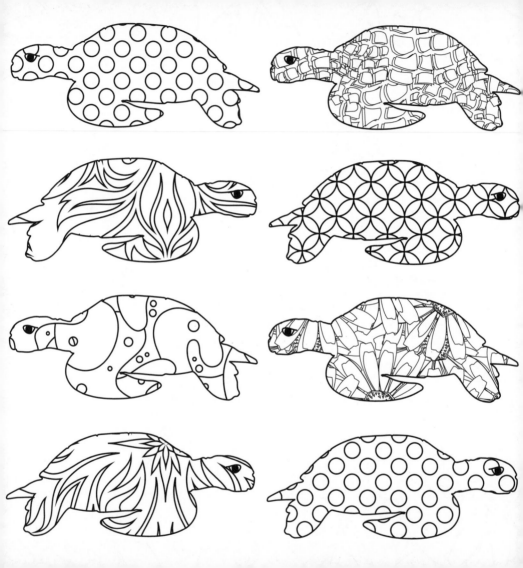

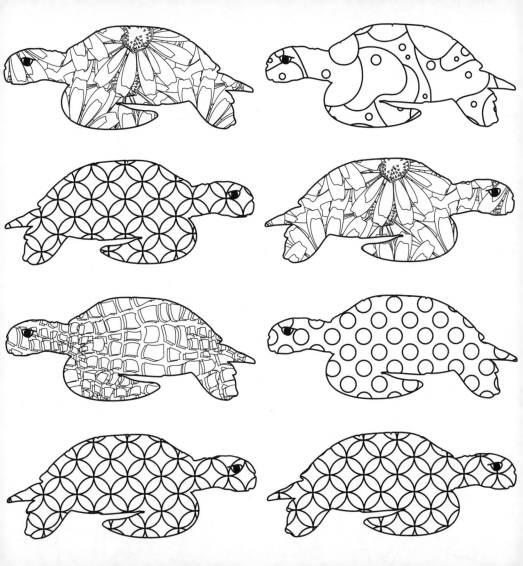

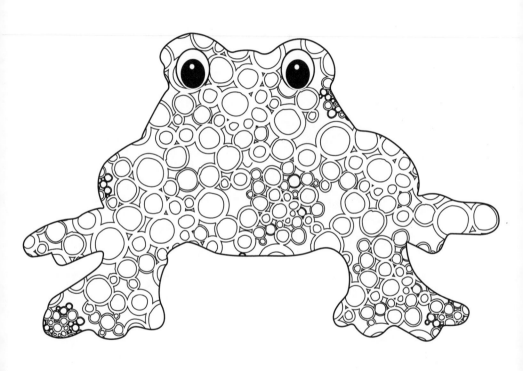

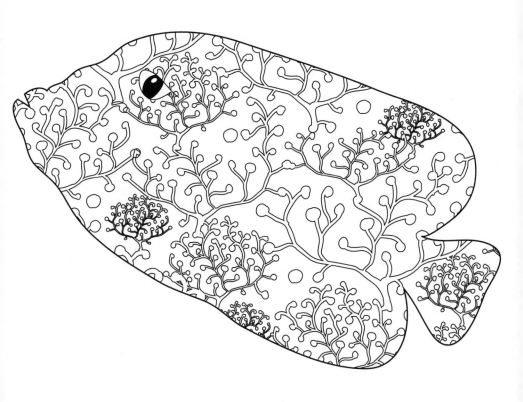

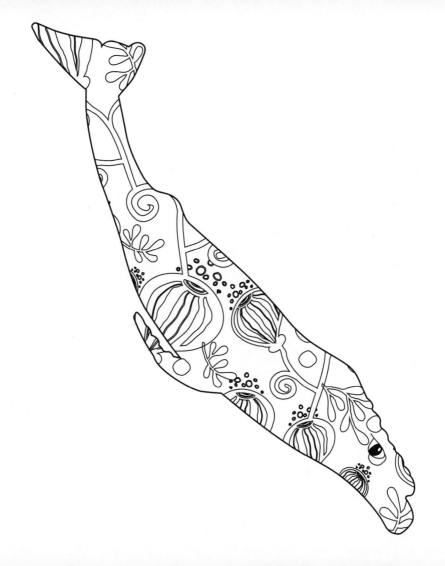

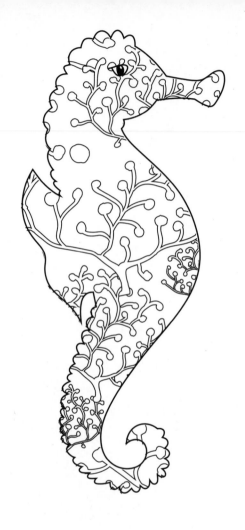

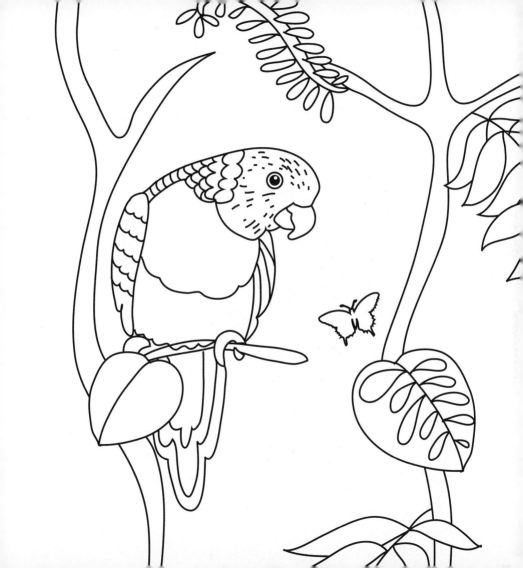

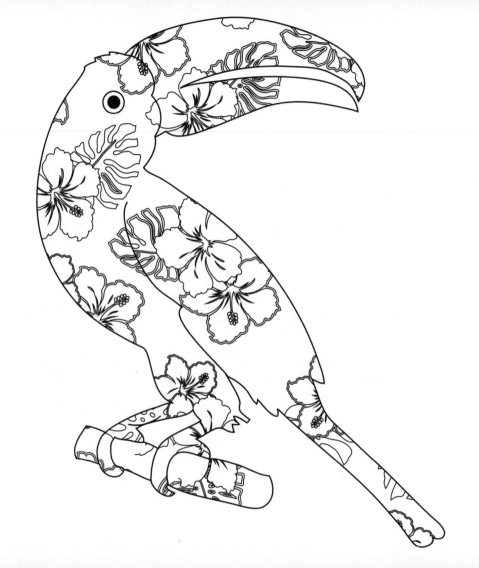

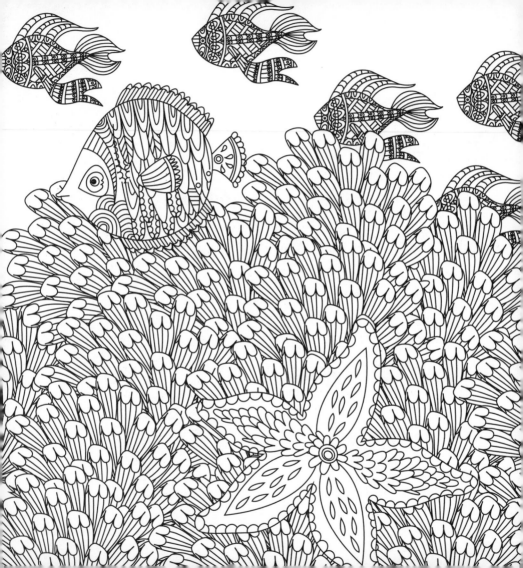

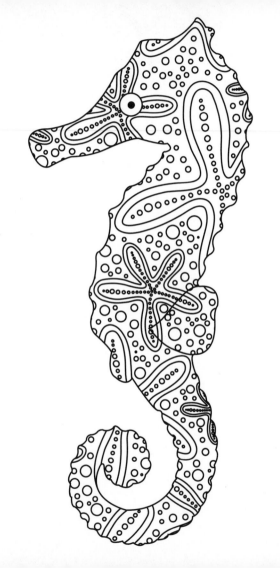

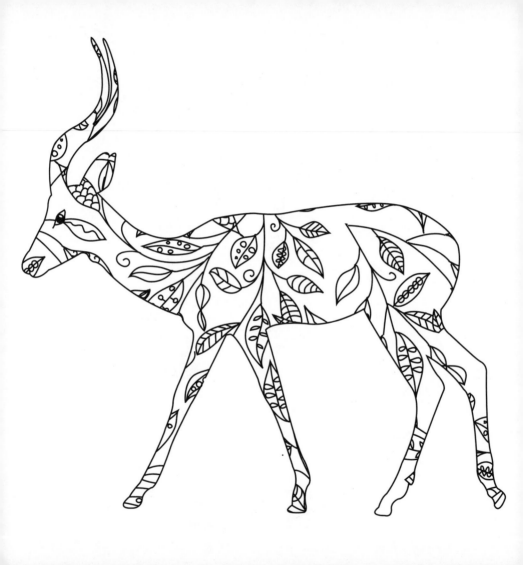